MEET THE MENACES OF BEANOTOWN

DENNIS THE MENACE

THE MOST MENACING RESIDENT OF BEANOTOWN! HIS STRIPED JERSEY STRIKES FEAR IN THE HEART OF PRETTY MUCH EVERYONE! OFTEN TO BE SEEN WITH HIS CATAPULT AND PET DOG, GNASHER, BY HIS SIDE, DENNIS HAS THE ABILITY TO CAUSE CHAOS IN AN EMPTY ROOM... AND HAS DONE SO ON SEVERAL OCCASIONS!

GNASHER

GNASHER IS A RARE BREED OF DOG – AN ABYSSINIAN WIRE-HAIRED TRIPE HOUND, TO BE EXACT! HE'S ALSO DENNIS'S BEST FRIEND. HIS TEETH ARE THE STRONGEST THINGS ON EARTH, AS MANY A POSTIE CAN TESTIFY! HIS HOBBIES INCLUDE PILFERING SAUSAGES ANY WAY HE CAN!

MINNIE THE MINX

SHE'S THE GINGER NINJA. IT'S ALL-ACTION ALL THE TIME WITH MINNIE THE MINX. SHE DOESN'T KNOW THE MEANING OF THE WORD 'FEAR' – OR LOTS OF OTHER WORDS BECAUSE SHE NEVER PAYS ATTENTION IN CLASS!

ROGER THE DODGER

IF THERE'S HARD WORK TO GET OUT OF, ROGER'S YOUR MAN... ERM... BOY! HE KNOWS EVERY DODGE IN THE BOOK. ALTHOUGH, SOMETIMES HIS DODGES END UP BEING MORE WORK THAN WHAT HE'S DODGING!

BASH STREET KIDS

IF YOU THOUGHT SCHOOL WAS DULL, YOU'VE NOT BEEN TO SCHOOL WITH THE BASH STREET KIDS! THEIR LEADER IS DANNY, THEN THERE'S PLUG, FATTY, 'ERBERT, SMIFFY, SPOTTY, WILFRID AND TWINS, TOOTS AND SIDNEY. THEY PUT THE 'COOL' INTO 'SCHOOL'!

LITTLE PLUM

HE'S THE LITTLE BRAVE WHO WISHES HE WAS A LITTLE MORE BRAVE! HE'S A MEMBER OF THE SMELLYFEET TRIBE, LED BY CHIEFY. WHY HE HAS A WHITE NOSE, NOBODY KNOWS!

NUMSKULLS

EVER WONDERED WHY YOUR BODY OFTEN DOES WEIRD THINGS? WELL, BLAME YOUR NUMSKULLS! WE ALL HAVE THEM, WE JUST CAN'T SEE THEM! THERE'S BRAINY, SNITCH, RADAR, BLINKY AND CRUNCHER!

BILLY WHIZZ

DID YOU JUST BLINK? THEN YOU PROBABLY JUST MISSED BILLY WHIZZ! HE'S THE FASTEST LIVING THING ON THE PLANET... AND POSSIBLY THE GALAXY!

BANANAMAN

WHEN DISASTER STRIKES, WHO ARE YOU GONNA CALL? NOT BANANAMAN, THAT'S FOR SURE! HE'S A FRUIT-LOVING, FRUITLOOP OF A SUPERHERO OTHERWISE KNOWN AS YOUNG ERIC. WHEN ERIC EATS A BANANA, HE TURNS INTO BANANAMAN.... WE DON'T KNOW HOW, HE JUST DOES!

THE THREE BEARS

THE THREE BEARS - PA, MA AND TED, LIVE ON THE PRAIRIE AND HAVE ONE GOAL IN LIFE - TO PILFER FOOD! MORE SPECIFICALLY, FOOD FROM LONG-SUFFERING HANK'S STORE. (HIS NAME'S NOT ACTUALLY LONG SUFFERING HANK, BY THE WAY... IT'S JUST HANK.)

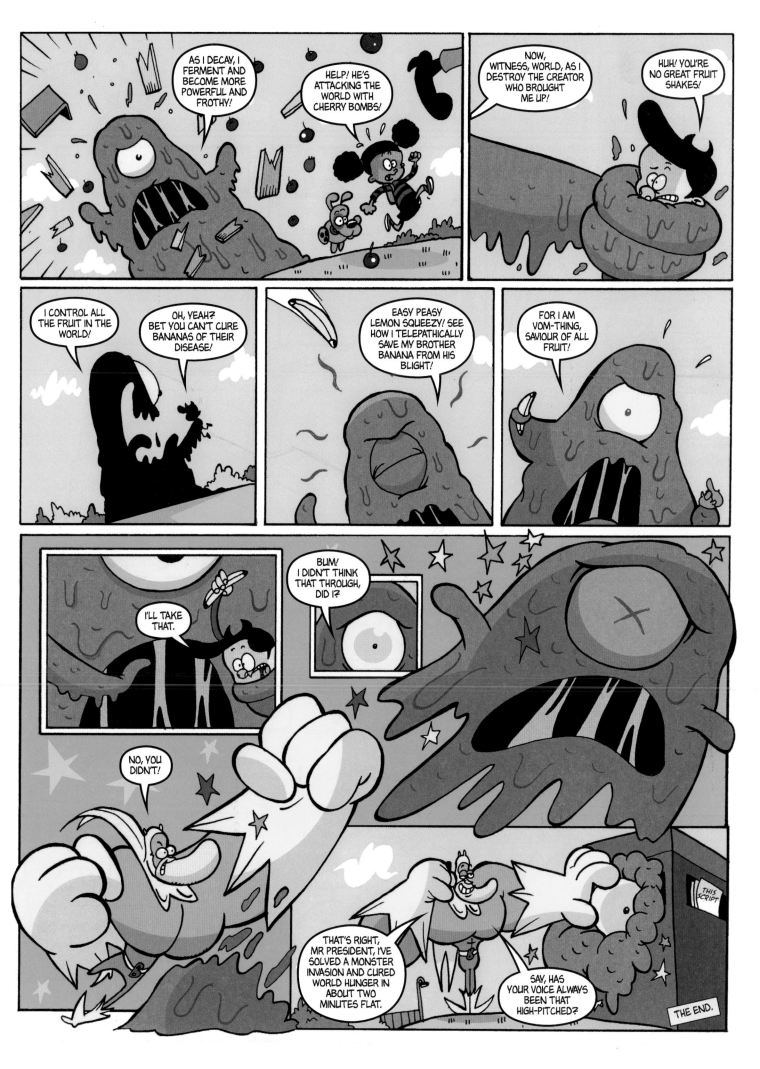

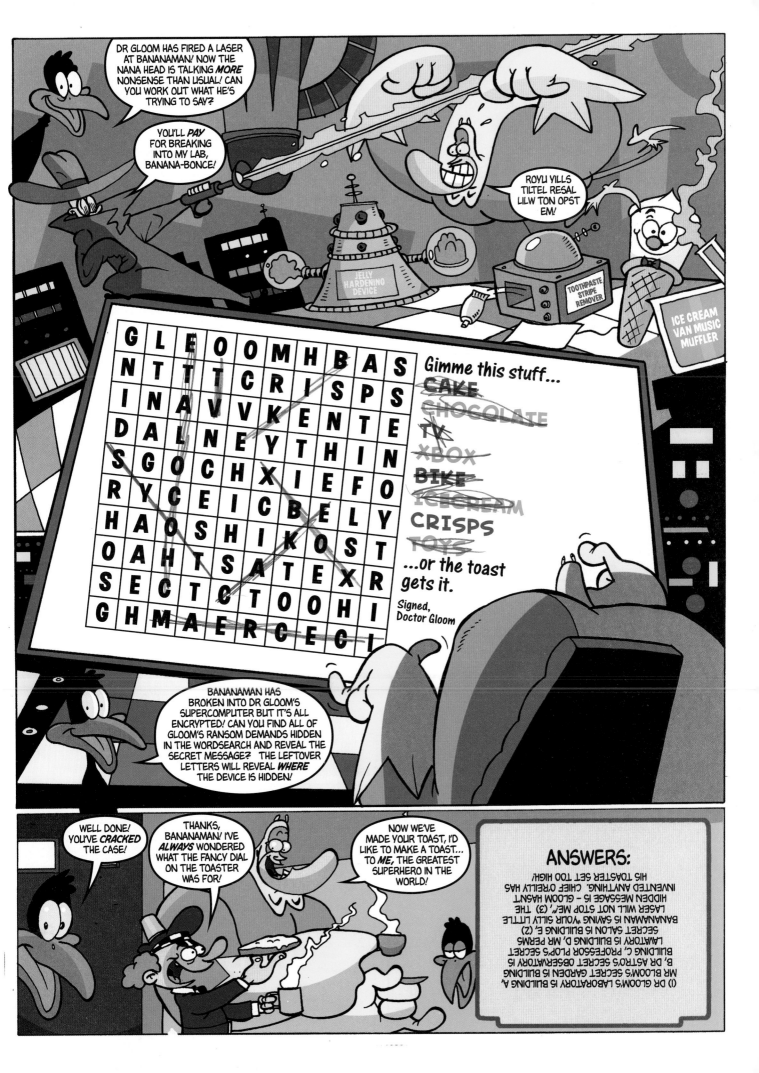

THE 3 BEARS

GEE, WHAT'S GOING ON AT HANK'S STORE? NEVER SEEN IT SO BUSY!

HANK'S STORE

LET'S GO TAKE A LOOK, PA!

WHAT'S ALL THIS, HANK? WHAT'S WITH ALL THESE PEOPLE?

WELL, NOT THAT IT'S ANY OF YOUR BUSINESS, BUT IT'S ALL THANKS TO MY LATEST GENIUS MONEY-MAKING SCHEME!

I'VE LAUNCHED THIS HERE CLUBCARD, THAT GIVES CUSTOMERS POINTS EVERY TIME THEY SPEND IN STORE! THEN THEY CAN USE THOSE POINTS TO GET FREE FOOD!

FREE FOOD?!!? WE'LL TAKE ONE - WE'RE ALWAYS USING THE STORE!

YEAH, BUT YOU DON'T GET POINTS FOR STEALIN', YA VARMINTS...

OW!

... BUT IF IT'S POINTS YA WANT, TRY THESE! HA-HA!

YOWCH!

EEK!

OWCH! THAT HANK'S A MEAN OL' PEST!

DON'T WORRY, SON O' MINE! I'VE GOT AN IDEA TO TEACH HIM A LESSON!

HELLO, MY GOOD MAN! I WOULD LIKE TO TAKE ADVANTAGE OF THIS FREE FOOD OFFER YOU HAVE GOING ON!

HA! DO YOU HAVE A CLUBCARD, 'SIR'? HAW! HAW!

BEAN

SHUCKS, YOU GOT ME! I AIN'T GOT A CARD...

... BUT I DO HAVE A CLUB! HEE-HEE!

WHACK!

OOOOOFYAH!

BEAN

HEE-HEE! THANKS FOR THE FREEBIES, HANK!

HANK'S ST

CORN FLAKES

BLEEEURRGH! OH, WHAT'S THE POINT?

RASHER

PANSY POTTER

PUP PARADE

LORD SNOOTY

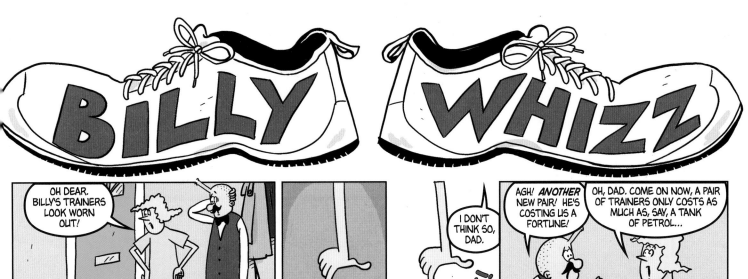

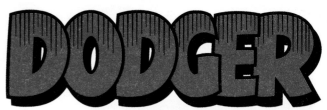

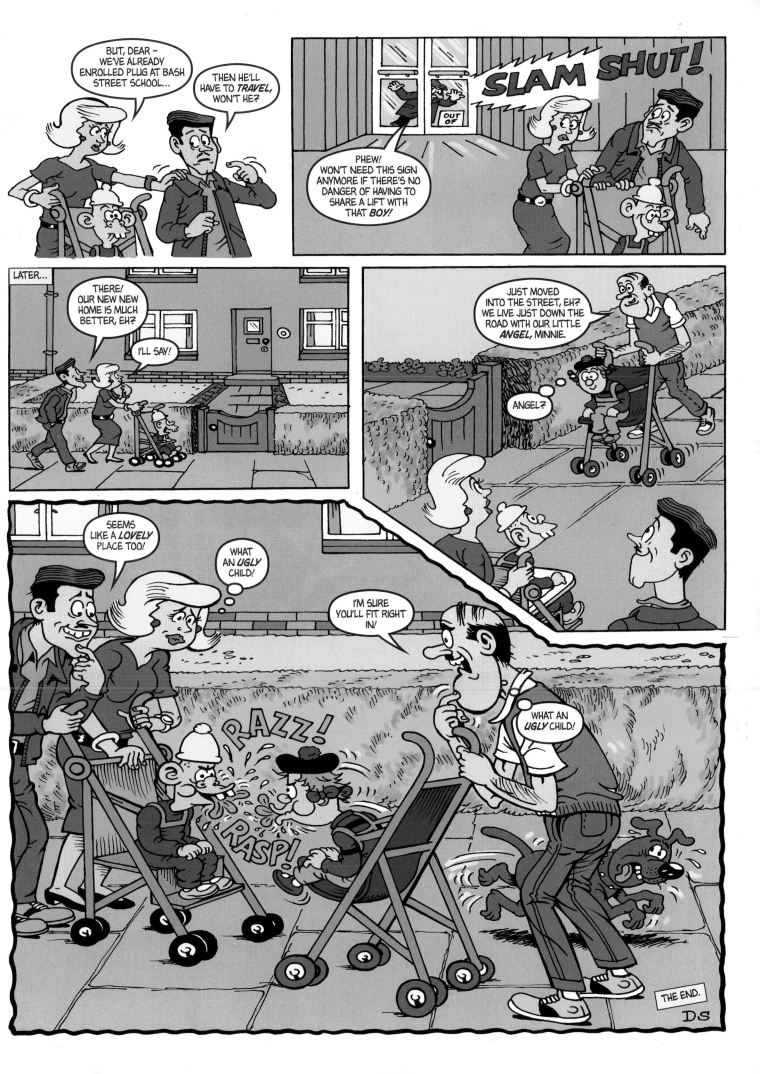

RASHER

PANSY POTTER

PUP PARADE

LORD SNOOTY

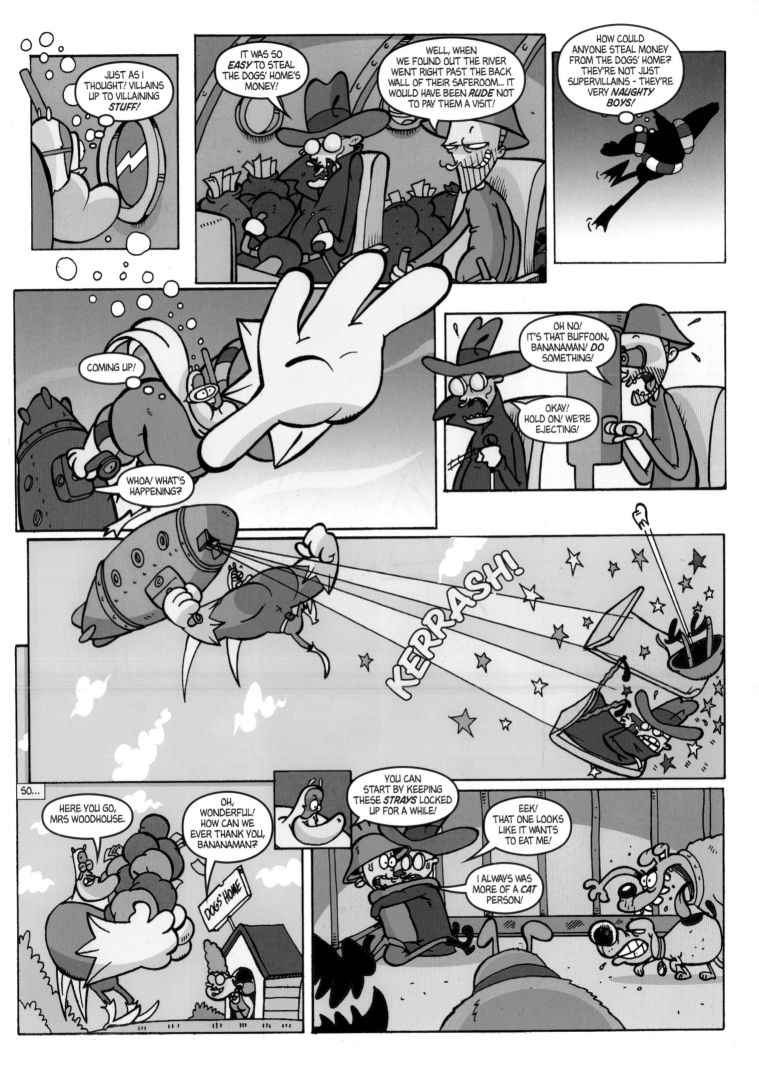

BILLY WHIZZ

BILLY AND HIS COUSIN, BILLIE ARE GOING FOR A JOG...

IT'S A BIT *HOT* FOR RUNNING, BILLY.

IT'S *NEVER* TOO HOT FOR RUNNING.

HUH!?

HA-HA-HA-HA! YOU'VE SWEATED SO MUCH YOUR SHORTS ARE *TOO BIG* FOR YOU!

BOFF

MAYBE IT *IS* A BIT HOT.

LET'S GO TO THE SWIMMING POOL TO COOL OFF.

GREAT IDEA, BILLIE. I NEED TO *CHILL* OUT!

TOOMF

POOL

CLOSED!

NIGHTMARE!

WE COULD GO DOWN TO BEANOTOWN BEACH AND *COOL* OFF IN THE SEA!

YAY! RACE YA!

WOO-HOO!

LAST ONE IN IS A ROTTEN EGG!

AAAARGH! A JELLYFISH!

THIS ONE IS TOUGH! FIRST YOU, HAVE TO FIND ALL OF THE WORDS IN THE WORDSEARCH!
BUT THAT'S NOT ALL — ONE OF THE WORDS APPEARS FOUR TIMES!
PUT THAT WORD IN THE KEY UNDER THE WORDSEARCH TO UNLOCK THE SAFE!

Q	W	S	N	E	D	R	T	Y	C	U	E	I	O	P
R	A	K	R	O	W	E	M	O	H	T	S	D	D	F
G	E	H	D	E	I	J	K	L	A	R	Z	X	O	C
V	P	G	B	N	L	T	M	L	O	O	Q	W	D	E
R	E	R	D	T	Y	U	N	U	S	U	I	O	G	P
R	N	A	S	O	D	F	R	E	G	B	H	J	E	K
L	C	Z	X	C	D	V	N	B	T	L	N	M	R	Q
W	I	E	R	T	Y	I	U	I	O	E	P	A	S	D
F	L	G	H	J	L	K	L	Z	X	C	D	V	B	N
M	Q	W	D	O	D	G	E	R	E	R	T	Y	U	I

WORDS —
~~HOMEWORK~~
~~DETENTION~~
~~LATE~~
LINES
~~DODGER~~
~~PENCIL~~
RULERS
~~TROUBLE~~
~~CHAOS~~

DODGER

ONLY ONE OF THESE TEST PAPERS IS THE REAL THING — WHICH ONE IS IT?

1. TEXT PAPERS
2. TEZT PAPERS
3. TEST PAUPERS
4. TEST PAYPERS
5. TEST PAPERS
6. PEST TAPERS

RIGHT! ON WITH THE STORY!

NOW YOU'VE SOLVED ALL OF THE PUZZLES — IT'S TIME TO GET OUT OF HERE BEFORE TEACHER COMES BACK!

The THREE BEARS

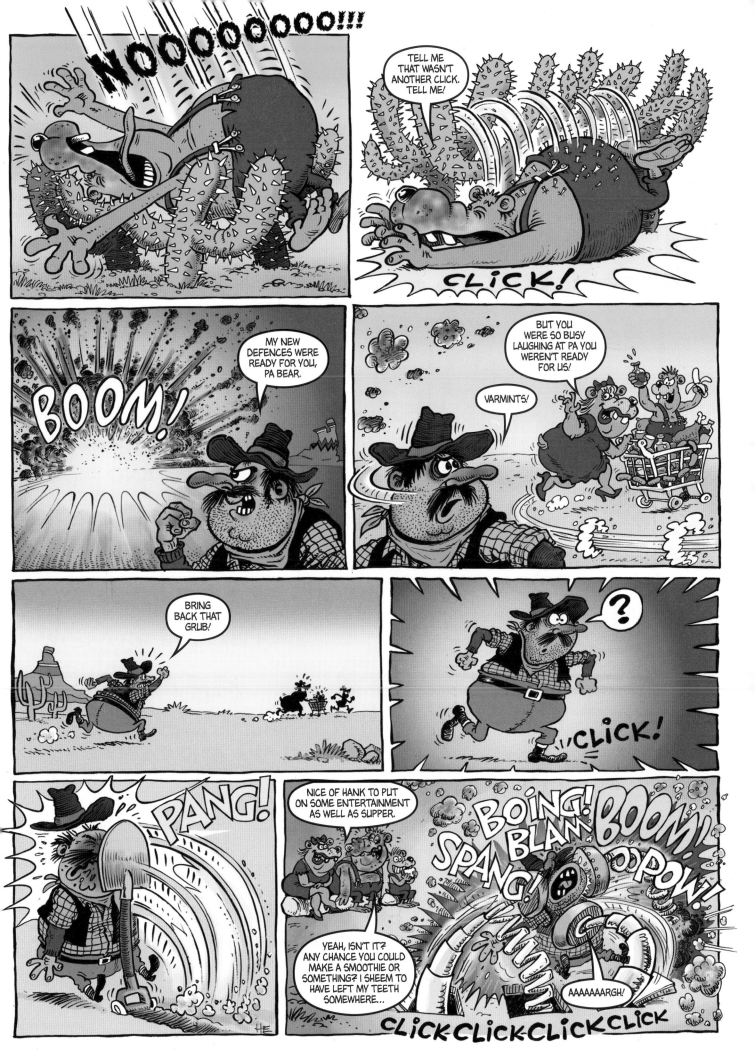

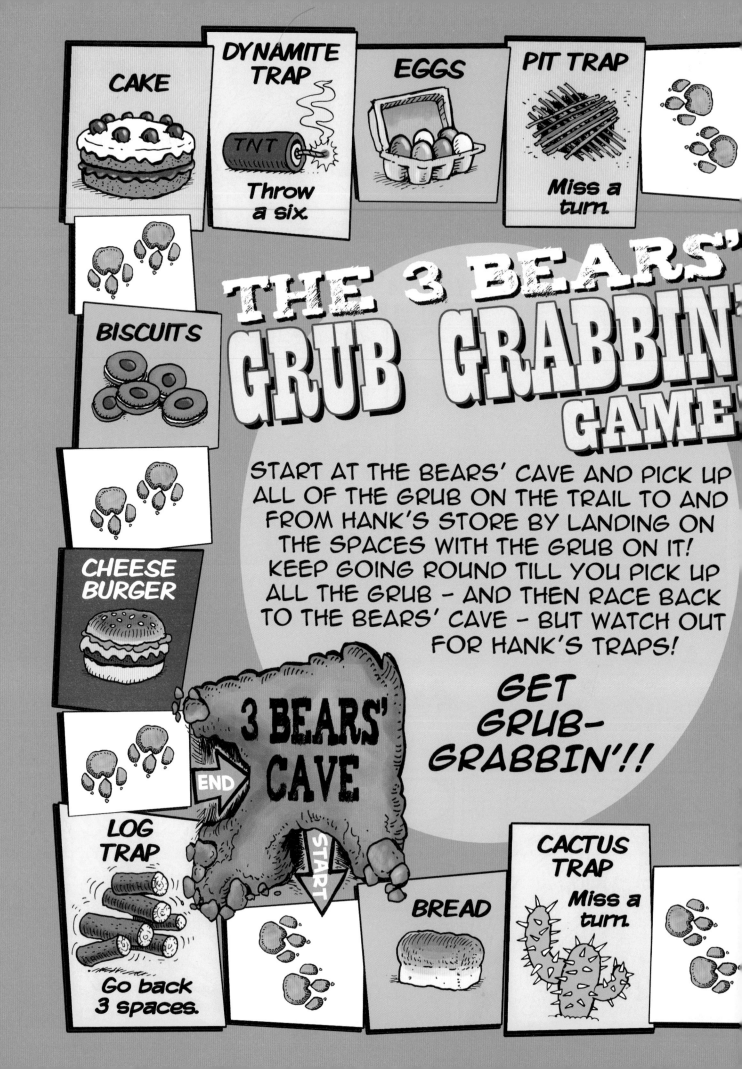

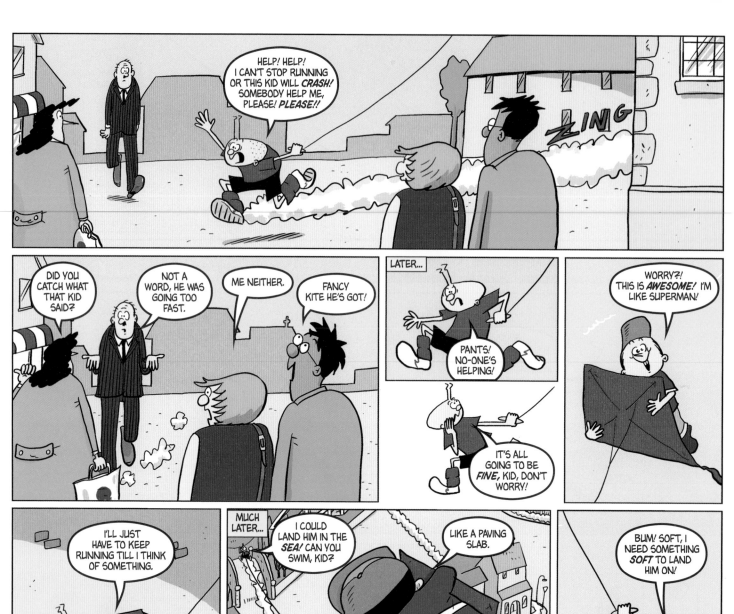

BOUNCE!
BOUNCE!
BOUNCE!

FATTY DIDN'T THOUGH.

FLATTEN!

BIKES ARE HARD TO CONTROL – IT SHOULD BE EASIER WITH JUST ONE WHEEL.

SQUASH!

AND...

THEN...

FINALLY...

VRRRRP!

BLITHER!

FINALLY...

IIB

STAGGER!

YOU'RE LATE!

DS

The NUMSKULLS

TYPICAL! BET THAT'S BRAINY WITH LOADS OF *OTHER* JOBS FOR ME TO DO.

DRIIING!

I'VE MEASURED THE TOE NAIL GROWTH. TIME FOR *LUNCH!*

SLOO... CHEESE, MY *FAVOURITE.*

SIGH. I WAS RIGHT. *NOW* HE WANTS ME TO MEASURE THE FINGERNAIL GROWTH TOO!

EDD'S LEG BONE

MANY JOBS LATER...

MOUTH DEPT.

FINALLY! I CAN *FINISH* MY LUNCH. BUT WHERE DID I LEAVE IT?

IT COULD BE *ANYWHERE!* I'LL NEED TO MAKE ANOTHER ONE... OR TWO. I'M STARVING!

SCRATCH!

THERE'S A VERY *CHEESY* PONG COMING FROM OUR BOY'S FEET, BUT HE HAD A SHOWER THIS MORNING. I DON'T UNDERSTAND.

SNIFF! SNIFF!

Cheesy Pong!

HOW COME MY FEET PONG ALREADY? I WASHED THEM TODAY. IT NORMALLY TAKES *DAYS* FOR MY FEET TO WHIFF THIS BADLY!

THAT'S WHERE I LEFT MY CHEESE SANDWICH!

WILT!

Barry Glennard

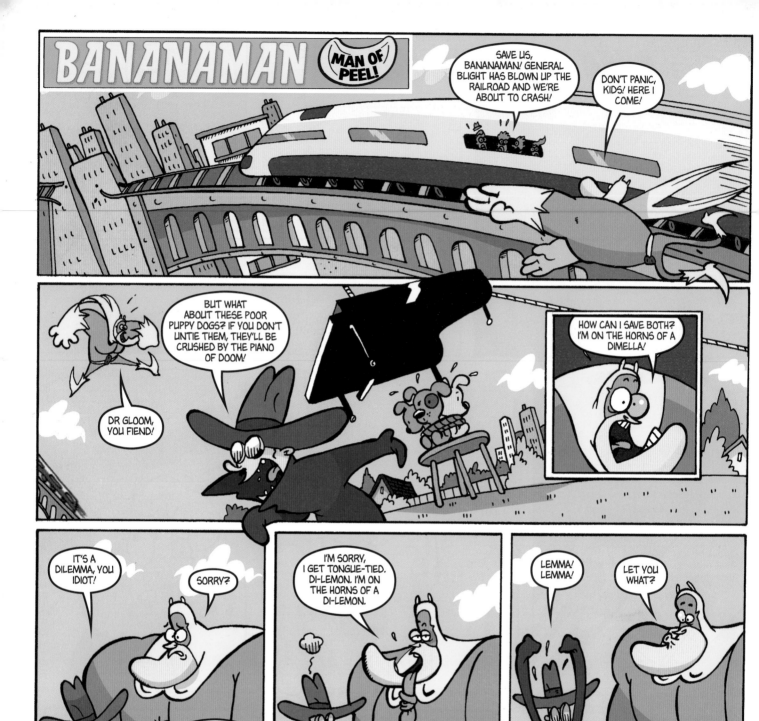

RASHER

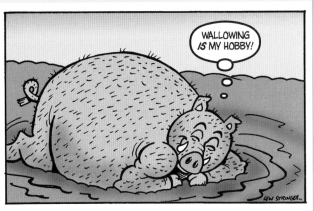

PANSY POTTER

PUP PARADE

LORD SNOOTY

THE BASH STREET KIDS

HELLO, READERS! WELCOME TO MY VIDEO BLOG!

RIGHT NOW I'M WITH SPOTTY!

SAY HELLO, SPOTTY!

DON'T PUSH YOUR LUCK, DANNY!

HE'S IN A BAD MOOD BECAUSE I MADE HIM DO A DARE!

BUT BEFORE I SHOW YOU THAT, LET'S SEE SOME OF MY EARLIER BLOGS!

I MADE THESE ONES AT SCHOOL – ENJOY!

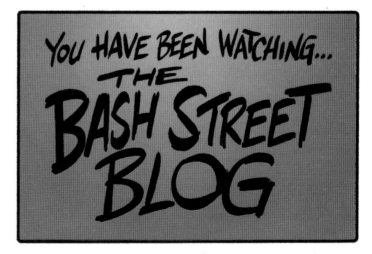

THE END

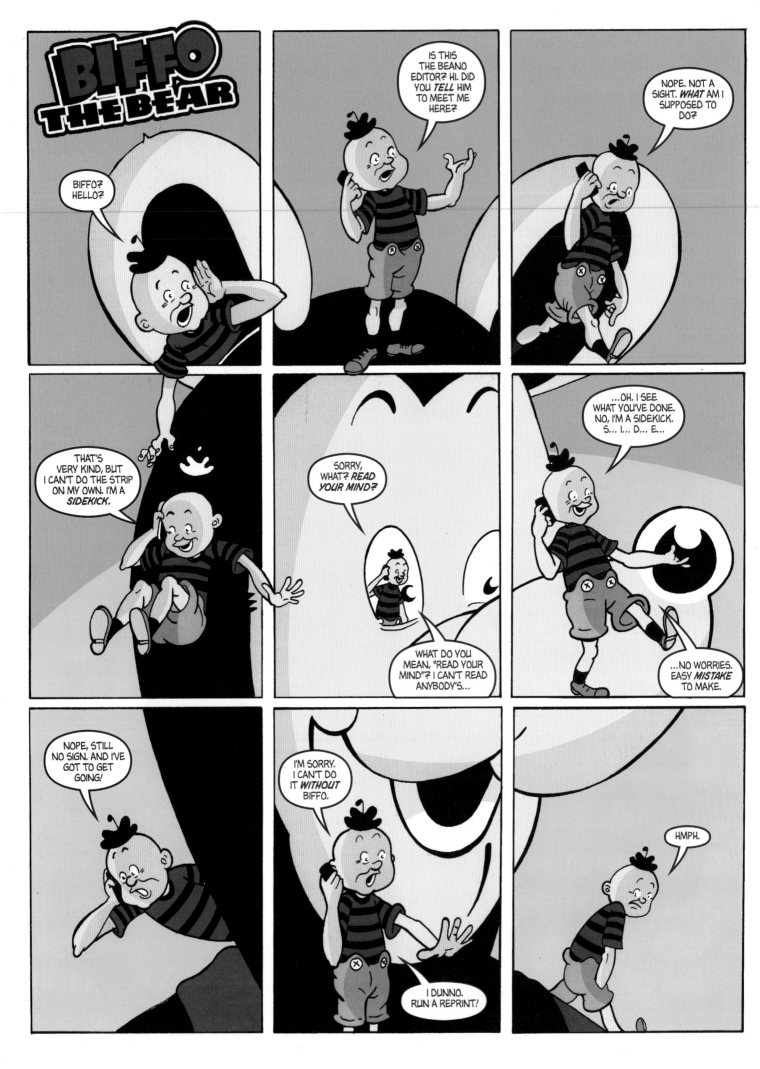

RIGHT, BILLY, WE'RE GOING FOR A NICE RELAXING DAY OUT BY THE RIVER, AND I DON'T WANT YOU SPOILING IT WITH YOUR ZOOMING ABOUT - OKAY?

I HEAR YOU LOUD AND CLEAR, MON CAPITAN!

BILLY!

ZANG

YOU PROMISED NO ZOOMING!

I'M NOT ZOOMING, DAD! THAT WAS A ZANG! NOT A ZOOM! SEE FOR YOURSELF...

NOW I'M RAZZING, DAD! NO ZOOMING, I PROMISE!

RAZZ

I GIVE UP WITH THAT LAD.

OH DEAR.

CHOO-CHOO BOAT!

BOATS FOR HIRE

ALFIE, I DON'T THINK...

BILLY'S NOT GOING TO SPOIL EVERYTHING WE DO! WE'LL HIRE A BOAT AND I'LL ROW IT, AT A GENTLE, RELAXING SPEED, AND BILLY WILL JUST HAVE TO SIT STILL!

SEE? IT CAN BE DONE.

BILLY, WHAT ARE YOU DOING?

JUST A BIT OF RUNNING ON THE SPOT! I CAN'T STAND JUST SITTING HERE, DAD!

YOU'RE GOING TO CAPSIZE THE BOAT!

ALRIGHT, ALRIGHT... CALM DOWN!

LET ME ROW WITH YOU, DAD.

BIIIILLY!!!!

BANANAMAN

MAN OF PEEL!

YOU GONNA BE OKAY AT SCHOOL, LITTLE ERIC? AW, YOU'RE SUCH A CUTIE-WOOTIE!

YES, GRAN, I'LL BE FINE!

I HATE IT WHEN GRAN'S LOOKING AFTER ME! SHE'S SO BLOOMING SOPPY!

HELP! THE BURGLARS ARE GETTING AWAY!

A-HA!

THIS IS A JOB FOR – BANANAMAN!

I'LL JUST REACH INTO MY LUNCH BOX AND PULL OUT A...

...BANANA SMOOTHIE?

GRAN!!!

MAYBE IT'LL WORK, LET'S SEE...

YES, FINGERS! WE ESCAPED WIV OUR LOOT! HEH-HEH!

WAIT, THUMBS, WHAT'S THAT?

IS IT A BIRD? IS IT A PLANE?

NO! IT'S...

WELL THEY'RE NOT GOING ANYWHERE FAST!

OW! A LITTLE HELP ANYONE?

RASHER

PANSY POTTER

PUP PARADE

LORD SNOOTY

THE 3 BEARS

"BEARSKIN"

GROAN! WE'VE BEEN OUT LOOKING FOR FOOD FOR *AGES!* AND IT'S SO *SO* COLD!

YOU SAID IT, SON! IT'S FREEZING!

BRRRR!

AWW, YOU *POOR* BEARS! ARE YOU COLD?

FUR-FUR-FREEZING!

WELL, MAYBE YOU'D LIKE TO COME AND HANG OUT IN MY STORE...

...DEAD OR ALIVE!

WH-WHAT?

APPARENTLY, BEARSKIN IS *IN* THIS SEASON! SO I THOUGHT I'D GET ME SOME TASTEFUL BEARSKIN RUGS IN STOCK!

AND... AND YOU THOUGHT YOU'D ASK US IF *WE* KNEW WHERE TO BUY SOME? GULP!

Vague

CLOSE! I THOUGHT I'D TAKE *YOURS!*

YIKES! RUN FOR IT, FAMILY!

B L A M

EEEK!

MUCH RUNNING FOR IT LATER...

PHEW! THINK WE LOST HIM!

GOOD! PUFF! PANT! HANK'S GONE *CRAZY!*

PUFF! GASP!

LOOK! *THERE* THEY ARE!

HUH?

THOSE BEARS ARE *PERFECT* FOR MY BEARSKIN SUIT! GO GET THEM, MEN!

RIGHT AWAY, CHIEFY!

3BEARS 2015 BEARSKIN 1

BANANAMAN
MAN OF PEEL!

UH-OH! IT'S BANANAMAN'S OLD ENEMY – AUNTIE...

IT'S TAKEN YEARS TO PERFECT BUT I'VE FINALLY FINISHED MY LIVING WOOL. HA-HA-HA!

GRR!

OKAY, MY PRETTY, I WANT YOU TO...

GRRRRR!

CHOMP!

DID I SAY 'PERFECT'?

STILL NEEDS A LITTLE WORK!

THE MOHAIR MONSTER GROWS INTO A CASHMERE COLOSSUS!

GRRRRRRRRRR!

LITTLE ERIC IS NEARBY THOUGH...

YIKES! A TURTLE-NECKED TERROR! THIS GARGANTUAN GARMENT IS A JOB FOR BANANAMAN!

WHENEVER ERIC EATS A BANANA HE BECOMES BANANAMAN...

I NEED TO UNRAVEL THIS WOVEN WONDER BEFORE IT DESTROYS BEANOTOWN!

GRRRRRRRRRR!

THIS SOCK-BREATHED BEAST IS GOING DOWN! THIS WOOLLY WRECKER HAS...

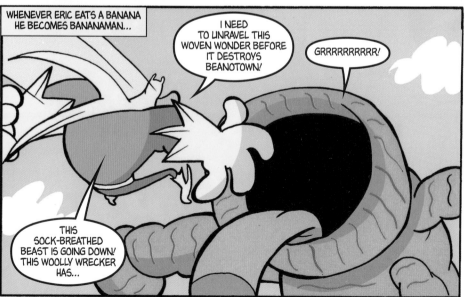

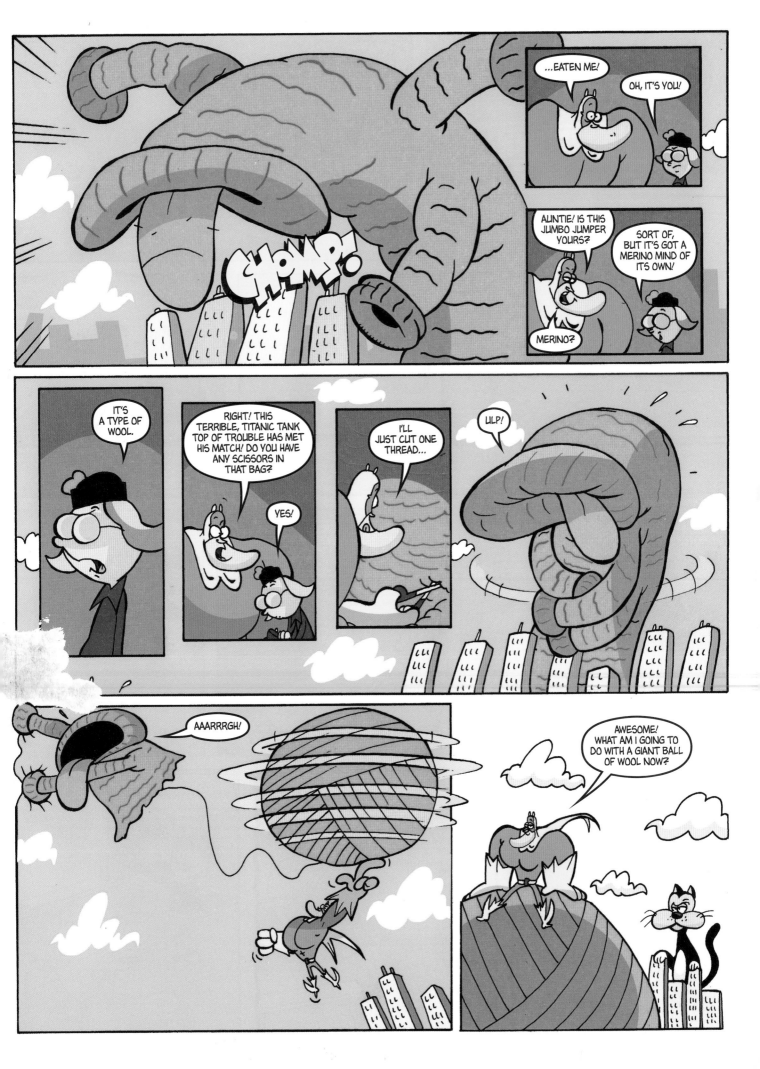

THE BASH STREET KIDS

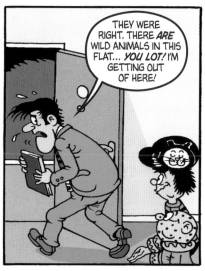

Dennis THE MENACE and GNASHER

'BYE FOR NOW!

SEE YOU IN THE BEANO®